HOPE STRONG

NAVIGATING THE EMOTIONS OF YOUR INFERTILITY JOURNEY: OVERCOME THE PAIN AND THRIVE WITH HOPE

CHRISTINA OBERON

Dedicated to our Lord and Savior, who is an ever-present help in times of trouble.

CONTENTS

INTRODUCTION

Did you know that hope is so powerful it is mentioned over one hundred times throughout the Bible? Hope gives us confidence that we can expect God to keep His promise. We cling to it in times of despair. Hope carried me through one of the most challenging times of my life—infertility!

Are you feeling like infertility is one of the toughest trials you've ever endured? Does it have you feeling lost, desperate, out of control, and questioning your femininity? If so, you're not alone as this has been my journey as well. The emotional impact can be the most crippling aspect of one's infertility journey due to feelings of helplessness, confusion, and failure.

This book focuses on some of the most prevalent

emotions associated with infertility and provides encouragement to cope, instilling hope to overcome such feelings. In my own infertility journey, I learned that attitude serves a profound role in successfully navigating such a trying time. The attitude we carry can make or break our spirit, which we must preserve in order to survive this journey. By addressing what you're feeling in the moment and then learning how to shift your perspective to one of hope and gratitude, you'll realize that you can not only survive such a dark time but also feel empowered to thrive in the midst of it. That's the hope this book offers.

It takes strength, intention, and repetition to operate from a positive place during a negative time. It took me years to learn the importance of maintaining a hopeful outlook and vision in my own infertility struggle, but once I did, everything changed for me. I was able to face and embrace the highs and lows of fertility treatments, unfavorable doctor's reports, and disappointing news without feeling blindsided and utterly hopeless. More importantly, I realized that once I learned to feel the pain, but not allow it to control me and to move forward with hope and vision, things actually started to go in the direction of my dreams, ultimately leading to a dream come true.

I promise you that once you find hope in your situ-

ation and successfully learn to cope with the emotions associated with infertility, you'll experience peace in your spirit. You are not defined by infertility. Hope is a constant pillar even in your darkest hour. "We have this hope as an anchor for the soul, firm and secure."(Hebrews 6:19 NIV) May you find comfort on these pages and feel the support you deserve during this season of your life.

ALONE: THE DARK HOUR

Forsake me not, O Lord: O my God, be not far from me.

— PSALMS 38:21 (KJV)

I'm all alone in this pain. No one understands. No one knows how I feel. No one can comfort me. Sound familiar? I remember these thoughts all too well. My mother had eleven children. My siblings combined have nineteen children. Understandably, I felt very alone dealing with infertility. How could anyone in my close circle understand what I was going through? Pregnancy had come easily to them. They had never experienced an intentional effort to conceive. Weighed down by the daily responsibilities of parenthood, my struggles to get pregnant may not have seemed to be as pressing an issue or one that they knew how to support. My situation was foreign to my family who bore children so easily that it was difficult to understand how deep the pain was.

Prior to undergoing fertility treatments, I often felt that even my husband did not understand. I wasn't even sure, some days, how *I* felt, struggling to put it into words, which made the feeling of aloneness so much stronger. On many days, the challenges surrounding conceiving led to isolation, clouded my mind, and sent me into a dark downward spiral.

Sometimes those closest to us are our greatest source of comfort and support. Other times, complete strangers who have walked the same path turn out to be the very source of strength we desperately need. I found this to be true in my journey. I was trying to deal with and process the situation alone, with the assumption I had no one to relate to, but as I started being more transparent, it seemed as though nearly every other woman I talked to had experienced some form of infertility. Over time, these conversations evolved into strong bonds and newfound friendships that carried me through many aspects of my journey, bonds that I still hold close to my heart. Looking back, I think practicing a little self-compassion—giving myself the kindness and care I'd give my closest friends—would have gone a long way. But above all, recognizing that I would never walk alone with God alongside me was the most important.

The National Infertility Association, RESOLVE, states, "Procreation is the strongest instinct in the animal kingdom. You are facing genetic and social pressure to have a baby. You are likely surrounded by friends, family, neighbors, co-workers, and a society who conceive easily. Infertility can be very lonely." You may find yourself having a strong desire to distance yourself from others, especially friends and family members who you feel do not understand or care or who are pregnant themselves. The frustration and sadness that you feel while others around you are celebrating their pregnancies can be overwhelming and lead to a significant feeling of loneliness and isolation. You feel like no one can relate to what you're going through. After all, how can they? They became pregnant. They're celebrating their pregnancy journey, choosing colors for their nurseries, and organizing baby showers. You aren't, and right now you just can't.

But can I tell you something? No one expects you to be a rainbow in a rainstorm. You're allowed to have days when it's all too much to bear and removing yourself from the outside world will be necessary. What's important is that you don't stay there. Remaining connected to the outside world can provide a sense of togetherness when you need it most. Other women, or those in infertility groups, can provide copious amounts of support during this time in your life. They help you to feel less alone during this journey and, above all else, help you remain hopeful. Being alone can serve you well when you feel the need for reflective solitude. However, try to not isolate yourself.

Hope in Isolation

You're in a delicate state and the people around you may not know how to support you the way you need. Some may have stepped back to give you space to process your feelings, or you may have thought it best to withdraw and choose solitude. However things play out, know that you are loved. Stay hopeful in the truth that God has prepared his best things for you (1Corinthians 1:29). Better days will come. And while the days seem bleak, there is a Comforter who will remain by your side, sending prayers to the Father on your behalf (Romans 8:26). Let this trust be a warm embrace that disarms your loneliness. You can depend on him to come alongside you to give you strength and upliftment at your most vulnerable moments (John 14:16). Remember that God's great love encompasses you, and he will hold you in his arms whenever you're feeling alone.

NOTES

ANGER: IT'S NOT FAIR

A time to get, and a time to lose; a time to keep,
and a time to cast away;

— ECCLESIASTES 3:6 (KJV)

*a*s a happy, bubbly, and overall optimistic person, I have always seen the glass half full, but after years of infertility, I found myself feeling angry and resentful, especially on hard days. Angry when I would see another pregnancy announcement; angry when my period would come; angry when I would get invited to another baby shower; angry when I would hear a mother complaining about her children; angry when a friend would talk about how hard being a mother was; angry when my doctors would give me bad news.

At one point, I would even become bothered hearing well-intentioned comments like, "Have faith," and "God has a plan." I suddenly found myself feeling easily agitated and on edge. This was not like me! I knew I didn't want to be angry, as it so often leads to bitterness. However, in contrast, anger is one of the most common emotions felt during one's infertility journey. Although it was an uncomfortable feeling, it played a role in my personal journey; it was an emotion I had to feel, let out, but then let go of.

Anger is a complicated emotion, as many other feelings can accompany it such as insecurity, jealousy, disappointment, and sadness. The central question associated with the red rage inside you is probably: "Why me? Why are there people all around me who can conceive (so easily it appears) and I can't?"

Anger is a perfectly reasonable response to the situation you find yourself in. In fact, anger can be a positive emotion in this case, as long as it's channeled in the right way. Anger can erupt like a volcano and sometimes that can be a healthy way to release stress. It can provide you with a form of self-awareness, which is a vital part of growing as a human being. It's important to remember that you may not be able to control the fact that you're in this situation, but you're definitely the captain when it comes to navigating the waters.

I once heard, "Things don't change until we get angry." When speaking of infertility, perhaps that anger will prompt you to look deeper into your health or options for conceiving. Perhaps it will help you discover and heal from unresolved past pain. It is important, however, not to hold on to the anger. It can eat away at you if you allow it to fester, which is not conducive to preparing your body to welcome a pregnancy.

You've got the willpower to change your attitude, to evolve away from all anger, and invite the energy of fertile success. See yourself overcoming the anguish of infertility, picturing most vividly the reality you long for—triumphantly holding your beloved newborn in your arms.

Hope in Anger

ANGER IS a feeling you may have to deal with when you're trying to handle difficult obstacles in your efforts to have a baby. When questions go unan-swered, your anger can sometimes lead you to look for something or someone to blame for your situation. In Job 42:1-6, Job's unanswered questions about his situation led him to become angry at times. If any one of us were in his situation, we might feel angry too. And like Job, we can also end up questioning God.

Frustrations can lead to anger, but frustrating situ-ations should also lead us to see that some things are simply out of our control and understanding. When God finally showed up, Job simply said, ". . . I have uttered what I did not understand, things too wonderful for me, which I did not know." The answer to all of Job's questions was simply God's presence. God's presence simply sends the message that though you may not understand your situation, you are assured that he's in control and that he knows what he's doing. You need not be angry at these unfavor-able times of infertility which are out of your control. Just trust that our loving, sovereign and all-wise God, who created everything, is there with you and for you, transforming your anger into a motherly force of hope and determination.

NOTES

ANXIOUS: JUST RELAX

Be anxious for nothing, but in everything by prayer and supplication, with thanksgiving, let your requests be made known to God.

— PHILIPPIANS 4:6 (NKJV)

"*J*ust relax." This phrase has been labeled as one of the worst and yet most commonly given words of advice given to women struggling with infertility. Each time I personally heard it, I would boil inside. How could I relax after years of infertility? How could I relax while on a strict IVF schedule that dictated nearly every aspect of my life, including rushing home from work to immediately administer injections at the same time each night? How could I relax when I was giving all of myself physically, emotionally, and financially?

A constant bubble of anxiousness followed me around, and the one thing I could not do was relax. But ironically, that is exactly what I needed to do. After all, being anxious would not aid in getting pregnant.

Anxiety is the overthinking and fear of future events, which I had absolutely no control over. I could plan, schedule, and act all I wanted, but I could not force an outcome. Releasing control (aka relaxing) releases anxiousness. I had been praying for God to take this anxiousness from me and when I discovered 1 Peter 5:7, it served as a powerful reminder of my role in eliminating this anxiety: "Casting all your care upon him; for he careth for you." This instructs us to *cast* our anxiety, meaning to throw it forcefully in a certain direction. Was this easy to do? No, and it took more than one throw, but it was necessary.

Anxiety is a universal emotion felt during infertility. All the poking and prodding, waiting for test results, feeling like you'll never experience pregnancy —it all amounts to a massive feeling of dread and disquiet. The anxiety can be constant, or it can come in waves. It can be a feeling of uneasiness in your body, or it can amount to panic attacks and a strong sense of despair. No one person experiences anxiety during the infertility process in the same way. Anxious bouts can be debilitating in the midst of infertility.

The tightening knot of anxiety in the pit of your stomach drains your energy, especially while you do all you can to have a baby. The thing is, this is the perfect moment to show how strong you are deep down inside. Show yourself how you can thwart anxiousness. Stop it cold in its tracks. Turn yourself around, and grow your willpower to break down the walls that lay before you on your journey to a baby.

Hope in Anxiousness

DURING THESE TIMES, remember this, Solomon's motto: "This too shall pass." And it will; time is an inevitable thing. Mindfulness is a technique that can alleviate the symptoms of anxiety. If you can stay rooted in the present moment, not fearing the future, not regretting the past, taking deep breaths, noticing all the good around you, you can get on top of the challenging and confusing emotions associated with infertility. We can find peace in knowing that God has already set our path.

The difficulties of getting pregnant can bring a lot of anxiety, for it's quite hard to stay calm when circumstances remain unchangeable, even after months or years of trying for a baby. In Matthew 6:25-33, Jesus shares practical truths that can address this anxiety.

First, he reminds us that we are more valued by the Father than we think we are. Despite how our anxieties may make us feel, we can trust that God values our relationship. Because he loves us!

Second, he reminds us that no amount of worrying or being anxious can solve our problem nor make us better. Dwelling on negative feelings doesn't help in any way. In fact, these may lead to more serious emotional repercussions. Rather than keeping these feelings, Jesus desires for us to remain secure in the truth that the Father knows our needs and that he watches over us continually. Trusting that he knows our every need helps us remain hopeful and overcome. So, we must let go of our anxieties and let God deal with what we cannot change for now. Because he cares for us!

NOTES

CONFUSED: WHY ME?

For God is not the author of confusion.

— 1 CORINTHIANS 14:33 (KJV)

a year into my journey, there were so many questions. Why can't I get pregnant? Why is *she* able to get pregnant? Am I not worthy of motherhood? Maybe I am just meant to be an aunt. Was it me? Was it my husband? Should we proceed to treatments or keep waiting? How do I know if I'm doing the right thing? Am I being punished?

The truth is, though, you don't know. You don't have the answers. And you may never have the answers. It is all part of the process, which took a level of patience I didn't think I possessed. I had no choice but to go with the flow. It would be years before I got answers to many of my whys. I realized through this trial that even when you get the answers you seek, there may still be confusion because you may have to deal with new information, which brings about a whole new set of questions. Over time, I came to realize that on the opposite side of confusion lies peace. And that is a much better place to rest!

How? What? Why? . . . But how? And then, . . . Okay, but when? These questions play on a never-ending loop for infertiles. We constantly question our own infertility. The fertility of others. The confusion associated with different medical terms. It is a feeling of utter confusion. Although frustrating, it is normal that we keep questioning infertility and everything associated with it. It's human nature to be inquisitive and to try to make sense of a situation, even if reason sometimes can't be made. The desire to be in control, a basic human instinct, is strong. But God's plan is not revealed to us through confusion. As we draw near to him in our concerns, he draws near to us and his plans are revealed.

Confusion, while contending with infertility, leaves you utterly vulnerable to doubting your natural ability to give birth to your very own child. But we must untangle the tendrils of confusion from that way of thinking. Remember, you may not have control over what's happening right now, and it's essential to accept that, but there are other parts of your life that you can control. You are in control of your thoughts and your faith—two of the most prominent tools that will help you get through this tough time.

Hope in Confusion

THE PROBLEM with persistent infertility is that it can push us to our limits, completely baffling us. We can become confused and discouraged when we are unable to find guidance and answers. But our "God is not the author of confusion, but of peace," (1 Corinthians 14:33 KJV) and he desires that we live with confidence and hope, trusting his wisdom and his guidance. When it becomes so confusing, you need to, "Trust in the Lord with all thine heart;" and "lean not unto thine own understanding." (Proverbs 3:5 KJV) So many things about your condition, you won't understand right away. So, maybe the best thing you can do is to step back and seek God's wisdom.

Don't let these moments of confusion lead you to

discouragement. Instead, let them be moments of God's leading and guidance, knowing that you can always find hope and strength in your "Helper, the Holy Spirit." (John 14:26 NKJV)

NOTES

DENIAL: I'M FINE

But they that wait upon the Lord shall renew their strength; they shall mount up with wings as eagles; they shall run, and not be weary; and they shall walk, and not faint.

— ISAIAH 40:31 (KJV)

*A*ccording to the World Health Organization, the definition of infertility is, "a disease of the reproductive system defined by the failure to achieve a clinical pregnancy after 12 months or more of regular unprotected sexual intercourse." For me, that year became two before I decided it may be a good idea for my husband and me to see a specialist. I didn't believe anything was actually wrong. I thought it would happen in God's timing, and I just needed to wait. I had spent the year previous changing my lifestyle, diet, and receiving weekly acupuncture sessions.

It was at the two-and-a-half-year mark when my husband and I finally saw a fertility doctor. The tests ruled out any issue with my husband, which obviously left me. I decided not to pursue any testing at that time and continue as we had. I think a part of me didn't want to know if there was a problem. I wasn't ready to face that truth or possible humiliation.

Fast forward to three years of trying to conceive on our own when it was clear, fertility treatments were our best option. My change of heart came through prayer and the realization that it was better to discover the underlying reason for my inability to get pregnant than to continue blindly navigating this trial. Sometimes we think finding out negative news will hold us back, but in reality, it can be a breakthrough to leading us in the right direction.

Perhaps you're in denial about being infertile. "Of course, I can get pregnant. It is my God-given right as a woman to be able to have a child. I'm healthy. I came off birth control a long time ago. There's nothing wrong with my reproductive system." Perhaps you are in denial about any treatment being beneficial. "I've accepted my fate; I'll never have kids. There is nothing I can do that will have a positive effect on the situation."

Denial is usually the first step on the way to acceptance. Acceptance does not mean you have resigned yourself to the fact that you will never get pregnant. It is about learning to accept the current situation and going with the flow, which understandably is easier said than done. Choose your doctor wisely. Choose someone who will give you honest information and talk to you about the realistic chances of achieving pregnancy. Counseling can be beneficial if you find you are in denial about any part of the process, from accepting current infertility to the potential outcome of treatment.

Hope in Denial

DENIAL IS the mind's initial coping mechanism in times of distress. This happens because not all people can be shocked and forced into accepting the painful truth or trauma that comes from repeated miscarriages or failed pregnancies. Some people need a "time out" to prepare and slowly ease the heart and mind into acceptance.

Acknowledge you're in denial and that you can take action to grow beyond it. Don't feel defeated when there is denial in you or in your partner. Rather, face it together with prayer, patience, and understanding. Allow in what your mind needs to successfully and sanely navigate the adjustment and acceptance of the pain, loss, and disappointment that accompany infertility.

Experience a breakthrough as you remember that God loves you and is with you. He is always close to the broken-hearted. Rest in these truths as you allow him to bring you out of denial and into confident hope and trust as you await the child he will grant you.

NOTES

DISAPPOINTED: HAVE I FAILED?

Nay, in all these things we are more than conquerors through him that loved us.

— ROMANS 8:37 (KJV)

We did it! We got through an IVF cycle. I was so proud. I had faced my fear and conquered egg retrieval surgery, producing fifteen eggs! What a rockstar. Now the fun part . . . waiting for results. We received the nurse's update that ten of the fifteen eggs were viable and seven of the ten had fertilized. Great! I felt confident and hopeful. Another few days passed and we were told only one egg matured. Wait, what?! One? How could that be? In a healthy cycle, approximately 40 percent of fertilized eggs grow to maturity, so how could that be? We had our hopes up for an even higher percentage than that, but instead, here we were blindsided and feeling disappointed. Our doctor didn't understand why only one egg had made it either. I started to feel the same way I did when my acupuncturist seemed confused by my lack of progress. I panicked for a moment, wondering if our IVF doctor would give up on me as well.

Disappointment is usually the result of expectation. But how could we not expect a great outcome? We had invested so much into IVF. We had put all our eggs in one basket (no pun intended). But we had come too far and I knew we had to keep trying. Reflecting on this part of my journey, I am in awe of God's beautiful master plan for our lives. The plan we cannot see or predict. That one egg that I was disappointed over—that we viewed as a failed cycle, that we thought should have been accompanied by more eggs—eventually turned out to be our son. It is possible that great disappointment can lead to great joy.

Disappointment can feel like a heavy piece of lead sitting in the pit of our stomachs. We can feel the lead drop deeper and deeper when we receive news during the infertility process that we don't want to hear.

The feelings of defeat and disappointment can sometimes be a continuing cycle in some stages of your life as you cope with a negative pregnancy result month after month. How many times have you felt like fate just keeps snatching away that thing that you want the most? How many times did it feel like what you've both been working so hard for only kept becoming harder and harder to achieve? We have all come to our wit's end at one point (if not many) in our lives, not knowing what to do next, and not knowing how to handle the next obstacle to conceiving that comes our way.

The feeling of disappointment may cause tears to fall. Let them fall! Be gentle with yourself. You are allowed to feel an enormous sense of frustration. You are allowed to cry, and you'll find what a stress reliever it is for you. Crying can also help your relationship with your significant other. Cry together if that feels good. It can be a beautiful and vital part of the infertility journey that people often overlook. If the disappointment is overwhelming, stop what you're doing—taking your temperature each morning, having scheduled intercourse, etc. can wait—and take a breather. Spend time on your other interests and passions. Life is still going on around you. Be kind to yourself.

Hope in Disappointment

Rest in comfort, knowing you're not the only one who has felt the piercing arrows of disappointment. Feeling disappointed shatters your future happiness, but there's always hope in your quest to start your family. Through this experience, you will evolve and change for the better, which will increase your hope for fertility success. You have it within you to give yourself the best possible chances of becoming pregnant. Because true empowerment first comes from within. It grows into an unstoppable force of nature. You can conquer this disappointment, and most importantly, give yourself renewed hope for the child you've always yearned for.

When you feel defeated, disappointed, and have no idea how to handle this situation, Jesus offers you a partnership. Lay your burden before him and let him lead you through this season of difficulty in conceiving a child. And when the failures and frustrations of infertility bring you low, find help and refuge in Jesus. He's ready to grant rest to your weary soul.

NOTES

DISBELIEF: HOW IS THIS POSSIBLE?

But Jesus beheld them, and said unto them, With men this is impossible; but with God all things are possible.

— MATTHEW 19:26 (KJV)

a major moment of disbelief came when I was told we would have to do another round of IVF. I had been so focused on getting through the various stages of the process that I hadn't even considered multiple rounds being necessary. When we were informed that only one egg grew to maturity in our first round, the doctor said it would be necessary to do another round to get more eggs. I apparently had an egg quality issue. How could this be happening? Another round of injections, another egg retrieval surgery, another grueling waiting period, another several months added to our years of waiting, another financial hit with no guarantees. Understandably, I went into panic mode. I can remember repeating out loud, "I can't do this. I can't do this." Well . . . I did do it.

When the disbelief wore off, my husband and I agreed that if we were going to do this again, we had to be all in. So I pulled myself together and used every resource available to educate myself on my body and the female reproductive system and prepared myself for the second round of IVF. For months I worked on improving my health and chances of conceiving, which resulted in six mature eggs in round two. It was surely God who gave me the strength to persevere.

The feeling of disbelief we can feel is tied very close to denial, but they *are* different. A lot of women experience a sense of disbelief during or after their infertility journey. They have accepted the fact this has happened to them . . . but still not quite believing it. "How did this happen to me?" keeps running through the mind. The flames are not as hot as denial, but the ash and embers of disbelief are still warm.

Disbelief may stay with you for a while, and that's

okay, as long as you don't remain in denial. Remember, it's okay to feel the rain without fear of getting wet. Watch yourself escape the feeling of disbelief as you create an atmosphere that will increase your chances of pregnancy. Disbelieving while conceiving is something all of us are familiar with.

Hope in Disbelief

A FAILED PREGNANCY or miscarriage may cause you to disbelieve life and God. You may begin to question what you know about him. Is God really loving and kind? Does He really listen to my prayers for a baby? Is God really able to prepare in me a healthy womb that can carry a child?

We all know devoted Mary in the Bible . . . even she disbelieved. She kind of had second thoughts about whether Jesus was in control of things because he was days late in coming and sick Lazarus had already died. She even cried to Jesus, "If you had been here, my brother would not have died." (John 11:21 NKJV)

Know that you can come to God in your moments of disbelief and share your thoughts and feelings with him. He is ready for those deep and honest heart-to-heart conversations with you. Don't hesitate, for even great heroes of the faith had those same moments of disbelief like the ones you are having now. Lay yourself bare before God and leave his presence with resolute hope as you experience him supporting you and proving himself a strong tower of refuge from the pain, from the confusion, from the disbelief (2 Chronicles 16:9, Psalm 46).

NOTES

DOUBT: IT PROBABLY WON'T HAPPEN

Casting all your care upon him; for he careth for you.

— 1 PETER 5:7 (KJV)

hat we think and say about ourselves has a profound impact on our spirit. I know this because, after so much disappointment, I was filled with doubt, and thus began the negative self-talk. I started saying things like, "My uterus hates me," "I'm not a real woman," "Maybe when I'm 100 I'll get pregnant," "At this rate, my nieces and nephews will conceive before I do." I would say these things and laugh but there was nothing funny about it.

Doubt creeps in to rob us of believing that what we hope for and desire won't come to pass. I used these statements to mask my hurt, unbelief, and fear that the worst possible outcome was my destiny. There is a popular quote that says, "Doubt kills more dreams than failure ever will." Hope is what keeps the dream alive, so refuse to bury it with doubt!

Doubt is an emotion that most people experience when going through infertility. Perhaps you doubt you can ever conceive. Maybe you question your ability to be able to carry a baby, even if you do get pregnant. Perhaps you doubt your doctors and the information they're giving you. Perhaps you even question your partner's commitment to you or the process.

Doubt is no stranger to any of us here. Ever since the beginning of our long, winding road of infertility, we've experienced the very nooks and crannies of doubt. We've doubted ourselves into oblivion. And we know how to cast it out! Weave golden threads of hope into the tapestry of your infertile lifestyle. Focus on the promise of motherhood, to make your fabric shine with all the happiness to foster fertility.

When you doubt that you'll ever cradle your own beloved newborn, it's okay. I understand your reaction. I've experienced the same thoughts while dealing with infertility. Don't feel guilty for having these doubts. The opposite of doubt is trust, and that's where you should aim to get back to. Trust your body, trust your doctors, trust your partner. Prayer and meditation are very powerful tools to help you regain trust. They help you have confidence in yourself and gain the clarity to trust in those who are important to you.

Hope in Doubt

DOUBT CAN COME when you don't receive the desired result to your prayers for a child. When your struggles and pleas go unanswered for a long time, your doubts may grow even more. When doubts come, you need to let your knowledge and experience of God bring you back to understanding and trust. In times of great doubt, re-acquaint yourself with the higher power who can bring healing and health to your barren womb. He can truly dispel your doubts and do amazing things before your eyes. Don't doubt but trust.

Let a deeper understanding of who God is rid your

heart and mind of whatever doubts you have in this stage of infertility. And while you await the child you've been praying for, believe and hope with all your heart that he remains steadfast in his love for you.

NOTES

ENVIOUS: WHY NOT ME?

Search me, O God, and know my heart: try me, and know my thoughts: And see if there be any wicked way in me, and lead me in the way everlasting.

— PSALM 139:23-24 (KJV)

*A*bout two and a half years into infertility, I remember stopping at the grocery store after work. I filled my basket and proceeded to the checkout line. A pregnant woman entered the line behind me. I took one look, put my basket down, and left the store without my groceries. I went to my car and cried. What made her more special, more worthy than me to carry a child? Having these thoughts made me feel awful, but I couldn't help it at that moment. It was not fair.

I was well aware of the very true statement, "Comparison is the thief of joy," but my usual confidence and self-assuredness seemed to be fading, and I began comparing myself to other women. I had all these plans and ideas in my head of being pregnant and feeling like a "real woman," carrying a child and all that comes with it: buying maternity clothes, having my husband look at me adoringly, taking cute photos of my baby bump, and planning a baby shower. Instead, I was watching other women experiencing all those things. But who was I to say who was and was not deserving of the blessing I longed for? It was also unfair to assume a pregnancy or children had come easily to others, as I did not know what they had endured on their journey to motherhood.

I had to ask God to cleanse my heart of these feelings, and He did! Envy and jealousy are often things we don't like to admit. The emotion can be destructive and unpleasant, but sometimes it can serve as a great motivator as well. By the following year, when I would see a pregnant woman or a new mother with her infant, I would smile, and instead of wondering what it would feel like to experience that, I felt the assurance of a promise that I would. There is a common phrase in the infertility community that states, "I'm happy for you but sad for me." Remember that another's pregnancy success does not equal your failure.

All of us know what it feels like to be jealous. When we find in others what we desperately want but can't have for ourselves, we can become discontent and bitter. There once was a woman who frequented a park playground to watch moms and their children, dreaming of the one thing she desired the most, a child of her own. She regularly went, not realizing how envy was beginning to eat her up inside, hurting her even more. As with this woman, negative sentiments like jealousy will only worsen one's situation of infertility.

* * *

Hope in Envy

YOU SEE A MOTHER WITH A BABY. You see a pregnant woman. You see parents with three healthy children. You attend a baby shower. Your sister gets pregnant. Instead of feeling any sense of joy, all you feel is the envy racing through your body. The envy eats away at you and makes you question everything all over again. Instead of being ashamed of this emotion, honor it. Sit with your envy and acknowledge it is there. Then put it away and don't let it become an obsession. Tell a friend how you feel, talk to a therapist, don't attend every baby shower under the sun, and keep active in your other interests. The envy will pass, as everything does. With all your heart, do something that makes you feel good and focus on the positive aspects of your life outside of infertility.

When you're tempted to gravitate toward the negative, stop and bring your mind to stillness. Know that in Christ, you're complete. Don't let your struggles with conceiving a baby make you feel inadequate in any way. Refuse to focus on the things you lack, and place your attention on all you've been given to enjoy right now. Cultivate gratitude, and let it spark your hope and expectation of a child.

NOTES

EXHAUSTED: CAN'T TAKE ANOTHER STEP

Come to me, all you who are weary and burdened,
and I will give you rest.

— MATTHEW 11:28 (NIV)

When talking about conception, you have probably heard the phrase, "Trying is the fun part!" But when you are going through infertility, *trying* to get pregnant is utterly exhausting. After three years of trying, which consisted of a year of acupuncture, visits to a sobadora, and diet and lifestyle change, I was still led to disappointment when our IUIs failed, thus sending us toward IVF. I was beyond weary, and did not know how I would continue. I was too tired to do aggressive treatments; too tired to figure out how we would afford it; too tired to juggle treatment while working full-time and in my last year of college. I was tired of putting on a brave face. I was tired of being strong. I just wanted to rest and forget everything about infertility. The burnout was real. I knew I wasn't ready to give up, but I needed to recharge, so I took a few months vacation from infertility.

I laughed, I found joy, I connected with my husband, I lived without worry! With the highest hope, I used my mind, soul, heart, and spirit, gathered together in unity, to gently guide the feeling of exhaustion away from my womb. I remembered who I was before infertility, renewed my spirit, and aligned my mind and heart with the next chapter we were set to embark on—IVF!

You start off full of energy, with determination in your heart, and hope pulsing through your veins. But slowly, as the weeks, months, and perhaps even years tick on, you begin to feel exhausted. The fatigue consumes you and settles in your bones. Handling all the emotions, going through all the tests, feeling all the disappointment is tiring. You're tired of fighting your own body, tired of arguing with your partner, tired of looking at other mothers in awe.

It's time to revitalize, energize, and reconnect

with life. Take some time out for you. Pamper your tired body, nourish it with healthy food, indulge in a good book—escape. Escaping once in a while can be a healthy way to continue walking the infertility journey. Escapism can be the sustenance you need to keep going and achieve results. Feel the renewed energies of hope, and let it swell inside you. Invite yourself to put on your armor and fight the great battle.

Hope in Exhaustion

THE TROUBLES that life throws at us can be overwhelming. Every day, responsibilities can wear us out. Piling obligations can burden us to the breaking point. Above all this, we feel the weight of emotional and physical struggles that come from the difficulty of conceiving. These moments of infertility can stretch us to our limits. We can't help but wish for a personal corner or a place to rest—our own oasis. Well, God did, exactly, provide that for us.

Unlike temporary fixes, God invites us to a steady experience of his divine oasis. When you feel so exhausted, worn down, and burdened by everything going on in your life, Jesus invites you to himself to receive real rest. It is in fellowship with him, pouring your heart out to him, and crying about your struggles with infertility, that he comforts you with his presence, allowing you that much-needed rest and relief. So, know and experience that he is always there, ready to give you what you need. Leave his oasis hopeful and ready for the challenge of conceiving ahead.

Your promise of a child may be delayed but that does not mean it has been denied. Whether you've exhausted yourself physically, emotionally, or financially, learn to rest but not give up. And if you do decide to leave the dream of becoming a mother, know that your efforts were not in vain. They refined you in ways only infertility could have, and a beautiful life still awaits you.

NOTES

EXCITED: MAYBE FINALLY?

Blessed is the man that endureth temptation: for when he is tried, he shall receive the crown of life, which the Lord hath promised to them that love him.

— JAMES 1:12 (KJV)

My husband and I had finally taken the plunge and decided to start fertility treatments. We had just done our first intrauterine insemination (IUI), and I was certain it would work. Our doctor said, "I hope you're ready for triplets!" It sounded so promising, and without knowing the statistics on IUI, I felt overly confident in its success. I even went to work after the procedure, and my husband and I took a road trip that weekend to celebrate. This was it! Finally! I could barely contain my excitement. Spoiler alert: that IUI failed. In fact, the IUIs that followed also failed. While I don't regret the joy, excitement, and expectation I felt that day, I realize now that I had put my hope in IUI and in our doctor, rather than in God. No matter our efforts, he has the final say.

The beautiful thing about the infertility journey is that it's just as much about the happier, exciting moments as it is about the disappointing and sad. The excitement you feel when you've made progress, or perhaps when you finally see a positive pregnancy test in your hands can be a mix of utter joy and relief. You've worked so hard and come so far, and your efforts are starting to pay off.

Remember to relish in this feeling. It's crucial that you feel it just as much as you've felt the other emotions. And don't forget to share the joy with your loved ones and support network, as they have been a constant source of support for you along your journey. Give yourself the tingling, endless excitement you deserve! You're on your way, with the best possible chance of having a child. See how your heart sings, how your enthusiasm penetrates each crevice of your beautiful inner core.

We've thankfully felt this way countless times, felt the rainbows of jubilance that makes us float with fertile hope even higher. The excitement of fertile success is right here, surrounding us with a warmth few will ever feel on their pregnancy quest.

We're happy for you! We applaud your euphoria of optimistic fertility. You've CHOSEN to be happy. You've committed to being excited. It's a tremendous feeling, isn't it? And may it only grow ever stronger, filling your womb with all the joy you deserve.

Hope in Excitement

TRYING for a baby can be a fun-filled time in your relationship as a couple. There is excitement in the air and great hope for the future. You're eager and everyone is eager for you. You're not just the ones thinking of baby names, even family and friends want to pitch in a favorite name of their own. There's great hope and anticipation. And there's just so much love between you two and toward the little one who is yet to be.

The Bible instructs us to categorize difficult times as joyful days. Cherish and enjoy this season in your life as a couple. Be secure in your love for one another and in God's love for you. Let nothing spoil your happiness, not the waiting nor the delay. Refuse to be impatient. Refuse to doubt. Above all, always keep in mind that the joy and fulfillment you have now comes from the love you share with one another. And this overflowing love completes and fuels your marriage whether you get pregnant now or later.

NOTES

FEARFULNESS: WHAT IF IT NEVER HAPPENS?

So do not fear, for I am with you; do not be dismayed, for I am your God. I will strengthen you and help you; I will uphold you with my righteous right hand.

— ISAIAH 41:10 (NIV)

Me: "No matter what happens, let's never resort to IVF."

Husband: "Oh, definitely not. That would never happen."

My husband and I had agreed to never go down the *in vitro* fertilization road. It was too expensive. It was too invasive. It was for desperate people. Yet here we were, sitting in a fertility clinic waiting for our IVF consultation. Oh, the irony. Had we really exhausted all efforts? Both of us sat in silence, holding hands, running through everything in our minds that had led us to arrive at this point.

I had no idea what was involved in an IVF cycle. The term was so commonly used, but I didn't know anything about the process and I was terrified of becoming a science project. But what scared me even more, was living with regret—the thought of missing the chance to have a child. So there I was, about to embark on a path I had been sure would not be necessary.

I wish I could say that the fear eventually left during the process, but it didn't. I was afraid throughout injections, before egg retrieval surgery, during transfer, and all the times in between. But as the saying goes, "If you can't beat fear, do it scared," and that is exactly what I did. The courage to push through that fear was found in none other than hope.

Maybe you feel scared, too. You've reached a stage of your infertility journey that frightens you. Your thoughts are fearful, and dread is slowly starting to spread its web around your body. Fear can make us feel small and physically ill and can stop us from being able to move forward, feeling stuck. Fear paralyzes us.

Too much worrying over not getting pregnant sometimes leads to negative speculations and assumptions, which further leads to fearful thoughts. You may start to fear that you won't ever welcome a baby into this world. Or if you've just been through a miscarriage, you may become debilitated with fear the next time you get pregnant.

Try not to fear your body. Your body is healthy and beautiful. It has carried you along this far, and it will not give up. Try not to fear the future. The future is unknown. No one knows what it holds and worrying about it will only bring you stress without answers. Try not to fear the journey you're on. You're exactly where you're meant to be. Have faith that your path is being walked and happiness isn't far down the track.

Hope in Fearfulness

IF FEAR ARISES, take a breath and clear your mind. Calm your heart. Remember that you needn't live in fear because you can recover from trauma, finding empowerment toward fresh and new hope through the Spirit in you (2 Timothy 1:7). So, release your fearfulness of the unknown and of what you cannot control. Find hope in the truth that the Holy Spirit dwells within you and you can find strength and guidance as you weather the difficulties of infertility with all its emotional and physical struggles.

NOTES

FORGOTTEN: DID GOD HEAR MY PRAYER?

"For I know the plans I have for you," declares
the Lord, "plans to prosper you and not to harm
you, plans to give you hope and a future."

— JEREMIAH 29:11 (NIV)

y entire early experience with infertility had me feeling completely forgotten. I watched year after year as close friends and family members, some who had even married after me, announced pregnancies, and I would wonder what I was doing wrong. One memory sticks out in particular. I was at work, anticipating the nurse's call with the results of our first intrauterine insemination treatment.

The call came, and I snuck out to the hall to take it. My heart sank as I heard the words, "I'm so sorry. Your blood test was negative for pregnancy." I held back tears and headed back to my desk. Within hours, I received a message from a close friend that she was pregnant, and by the end of the workday, my sister informed me that she was also pregnant. Talk about adding salt to a wound! It was as if a joke was being played on me. Had God forgotten me? Had I done something wrong? Had I not done something right? It seemed like I was watching everything and everyone blossom except me. But this is where I was wrong.

I read a passage by T.D. Jakes that said we can't produce the fruit without the frustration. Even more powerful was his statement that "God is planting you in richer soil for greater fruit." Could it be possible that I wasn't being left behind at all, but instead something better than I'd imagined was in store for me? Yes! Choosing to believe that the best was yet to come allowed me to feel forgotten no more, and instead, expectant.

Many women feel incredibly forgotten when they're going through infertility. Do you feel forgotten? Do you feel like God has overlooked your struggles and woes? Perhaps you feel ignored by the fertility clinics you've spent so much time and so much money on. Maybe you feel forgotten by your friends who've gotten pregnant and are on the pregnancy journey. You want to jump up and down every day with a sign reading, "Don't forget about me! I'm here, waiting and praying for a miracle." Perhaps you feel the pressures of society. You're a woman who wants to have a child. But you can't, and that makes you feel like an outsider.

In these times, remember that everyone's path to motherhood is different and unique. Your path is not easy, and this is your challenge. And as the day turns into night and the night fades into the glorious morning sun, remember, you have not been forgotten. You can help yourself ease your stress. Become flexible to become remembered.

Devote yourself to exploring the unique and overlapping feelings of hope. Shake yourself free from doubt and self-judgment. Use your own sense of encouragement to achieve, to fulfill. Your happiness deserves to flourish; it's boundless and genuinely limitless. In your own space, at your own pace, revive yourself and expand your gratitude.

Hope in Feeling Forgotten

1 How long wilt thou forget me, O Lord? for ever? how long wilt thou hide thy face from me? 2 How long shall I take counsel in my soul, having sorrow in my heart daily? how long shall mine enemy be exalted over me? 3 Consider and hear me, O Lord my God: lighten mine eyes, lest I sleep the sleep of death; 4 Lest mine enemy say, I have prevailed against him; and those that trouble me rejoice when I am moved. 5 But I have trusted in thy mercy; my heart shall rejoice in thy salvation. 6 I will sing unto the Lord, because he hath dealt bountifully with me (Psalm 13 KJV).

What happens when your prayers and struggles to have a child go unanswered? When God seems to ignore your pleas, you may slide into that feeling of neglect or abandonment. The Bible shares in Psalm 32 how David felt that same way, and we can find resolution if we respond as he did. When God delays his answer and when you feel forgotten, bring to mind that God is steadfast in his love for you. Also, let your past experiences of God's goodness strengthen your hope. He is at work. You're not forgotten. God will continue to show you his goodness. He will show his love and favorable answer for you at the perfect time.

Just keep on pouring your heart out to him and allow his peace, which is beyond our understanding, to protect (literally stand on guard) your heart and mind (Philippians 4:6-7) and keep you secure.

NOTES

GUILT: IT'S ALL MY FAULT

Blessed is he whose transgression is forgiven, whose sin is covered. Blessed is the man unto whom the Lord imputeth not iniquity, and in whose spirit there is no guile.

— PSALM 32:1-2 (KJV)

$\mathcal{H}$ave you ever said something, and the minute the words left your lips, you had instant regret? This is what happened when I spat out, "Just go find someone who can have a baby for you!" Behind these hurtful words to my husband was indeed pain but also guilt. After a few years of infertility, I began to feel a heavy sense of guilt. After all, it had been determined that I was the reason for our inability

to conceive. I couldn't do the most basic womanly act
—get pregnant and have a child. But the guilt was
deepened by the fact that I could not give my husband
a child. I wanted more than anything to progress to
the next level in our marriage—a family of our own—
and I couldn't deliver. It was my fault.

Then there was the guilt of ghosts past. I had spent
my twenties heavy in the party scene, which accompanied a hectic work schedule and an unhealthy lifestyle. I convinced myself that I had created my current
predicament by not caring for myself as I should have
years prior. If only I had not partied so much. If only I
had not worked every day of the week and subjected
myself to intense stress. If only I had paid more attention to my reproductive health. If only . . .

What I came to realize was that I had created self-
imposed guilt, blameworthy standards that I hadn't
lived up to. I allowed myself to believe these lies for
some time before choosing to fight them. I chose to
extend myself grace and forgiveness. Doing so
allowed me to move forward in the journey with love
for both myself and my husband, and an understanding that nothing about infertility was my fault.

One of the ugliest emotions infertility can bring
out in us is guilt. Guilt often starts out as a silent

thought, settling in and attaching its dark roots to the back of the mind. Slowly, it starts to twist and wind its way all through the body, emerging in times of stress, tension, and pain.

Are you self-blaming? For the thoughts you've had previously of never wanting to have children? For the abortion you had when you were nineteen? For the sexually transmitted disease you contracted six years ago?

It's all about hindsight. When that guilt and self-blame kicks in, remind yourself of this: you made the best decision with the information you had at that time. You're not God. You could not have foreseen the journey ahead.

Hope in Guilt

WHEN YOU'VE LIVED with the condition of infertility for a long while, your mind may start to play tricks on you. It may fool you into feeling and thinking that it's all your fault or that you're not doing it right. Like some troubled couples out there, you may feel like heaven refuses to give you a child because you're not worthy to become a parent or that you won't make a good mother.

Banish those thoughts if they come. You know them to be untrue. And if you know God well enough, you'd feel very certain that they're never true. There is no condemnation to those who are in a loving relationship with the Father (Romans 8). He has nothing but love and support for you. Refuse those "guilty" thoughts each time and choose hopeful, happy thoughts. Because our God is a God of hope and if you let him, he will dispel those thoughts of guilt and fill you with his joy and peace. (Romans 15:13).

NOTES

HOPEFUL: NEW DAY, NEW OPPORTUNITY

Now the God of hope fill you with all joy and peace in believing, that ye may abound in hope, through the power of the Holy Ghost.

— ROMANS 15:13 (KJV)

In 2017, it had been three years of trying to conceive, a lot of unfavorable medical reports, no pregnancies, and the realization that we were on our way to the world of fertility treatments. But it was also the time that hope became my anthem. It wasn't a quiet thought. It was powerful, full-force strong! I kept hearing a steady voice telling me not to give up. I was no longer facing each day with fear or what-ifs. I felt joy. I knew I would be a mother. I no longer feared the medical reports. What was there to fear when I knew God's promise to be true? The only explanation for this shift in my spirit was that I had placed this giant in God's hands and he filled me with relentless and undeniable hope. Maintaining a hopeful and positive outlook took intentional acts, such as avoiding negativity and triggers, speaking kindly to and of myself, and reminding myself that God would not fail me. He knows what's best for us and will see us through to the end.

Every day, you wake up with hope, and you're blessed to feel this emotion! Hope is your best friend, walking with you on this infertility journey. Hope is often the hardest emotion to hold onto, especially when you need it the most. If human beings didn't have a sense of hope about anything at all (e.g., career, personal relationships, finances), then we wouldn't be a motivated race. The hope that you hold during the infertility process is the most important thing that will get you to the end.

Hope is different than faith. When you have faith in something, you have trust in something. Hope comes before faith. It is hope that wills you to have faith. Hope is what will get you through all the tests, scans, and results and will push you to keep trying. As Winston Churchill once wrote: "Success is going from failure to failure without losing enthusiasm." Go beyond, unfold the way you want to blossom with an inner sense of harmony.

Embrace who you are, treating yourself with kindness, good thoughts, kind words, and good deeds. Experience a more profound sense of inner peace because it's okay to give yourself credit for being aware of how you feel. Change your perceptions to alter your life and make your own winner's circle, then live in it! Believe in your path, soak in your journey, and fill it with a hope you've never known. Carry that great momentum with you and store it like an eternal fountain to fortify your life. Make life more fun, more joyful, better than yesterday, and better still tomorrow!

Putting Hope in Hopeful

LIFE IS mysterious and wonderful when you're hoping upon hope, and there is hope in hopefulness. Because we can be hopeful in spite of despair and resignation, we can blindly and reluctantly hope just for the mere sake of it. But God blesses a hoping parent who hopefully hopes for a child. (That's a lot of hope!) God brightens your day when you hope from an understanding that nothing is impossible with God. God surprises you with mind-boggling miracles when you hope out of trust and confidence that God is never out to spite you and won't ever withhold what is best for you. Hope sustains your hopefulness when you recognize that there is a purpose when the Father delays granting you a child. So, keep your hopes up and spread that positivity around!

NOTES

HOPELESS: WHERE IS MY FAITH?

Wait on the Lord: be of good courage, and he shall strengthen thine heart: wait, I say, on the Lord.

— PSALM 27:14 (KJV)

*B*efore I became anchored in hope, I experienced many hopeless moments. One specific instance occurred about two years into my infertility journey. I had been taking a holistic approach up until this time and was confident I would conceive naturally. One of the natural methods I had chosen was acupuncture with herbs. I wanted it to work so badly. I had friends who had great success after just several months. While it was a hassle to chart and track body temperature, ovulation, and intercourse activity, it was not invasive and fairly inexpensive, so I was determined to have it work. Why wouldn't it?

Even though it had already been a full year of acupuncture sessions, on this particular day, I arrived at my appointment feeling slightly nervous but excited for the possibility that this could be my last appointment before finding out I was pregnant. The needles were placed, heat lamps positioned, and lights turned off. I kept my hands on my belly imagining movement and life and smiling to myself as I napped. The session ended and the doctor came in and was reviewing my charts for the last six months with a perplexed look on his face. To my surprise, he then said very matter of fact, "You're taking too long. You need to move on to IUI."

I felt a lump in my throat and a sting in my eyes that I fought to hold back. What did he mean I was taking too long? It hit me that he was giving up on me. Had I just spent every single weekend driving hours from home, taking herbs, and tracking every activity of my reproductive system to be told that I couldn't be helped; that I was hopeless? The drive home that day was the longest, filled with a flood of tears I could not hold back. There was no hope for me.

It took me some time to pull myself together and keep believing that I had a shot at being a mother and that all hope wasn't lost. But I first had to recognize that I had been putting my hope in all the wrong places. My hope had been in my doctor, in acupuncture, in herbs, in what the charts said, in my body—completely forgetting where my hope should have rested all along, which is in the Lord.

The opposite emotion of hopeful is hopeless. Hopelessness is a natural feeling that usually occurs somewhere along the infertility journey. All hope is lost. You don't think you'll ever conceive. You don't think you'll ever be happy. This is not true. There is life after infertility.

Even though it's tough to pull yourself out of the grey fog, your body and mind will feel so much better if you focus on positive possibilities. Your body is reactive to your thoughts and feelings, so keeping it weighed down with despair is not helping your situation.

Hope in Hopelessness

THE CONSTANT STRUGGLE during infertility may sink

you into a pit of hopelessness. Hopeless because you feel like nothing you do to conceive seems to be working. Hopeless because all the obstacles to that one dream of conceiving seem to stack up like an insurmountable wall you just can't get over. Not everything will go your way and according to your own timing. And as you struggle through a long period of infertility, refuse hopelessness. Let grace and hope renew your strength so you can run the race of life and not grow weary nor faint. Remember, God can accomplish even that which seems impossible and hopeless (Hebrews 11:11). You see, our God is a God of hope and when you put your trust in him, you can overflow with hope even during this stage of child-lessness. In having this mindset, you can and will meet this difficulty of conceiving with fresh and sure confidence.

NOTES

LOSS: WORDS CAN'T EXPRESS

He heals the brokenhearted and binds up their wounds.

— PSALM 147:3 (NIV)

*L*oss wears many faces during infertility. The greatest being miscarriage or stillbirth. These are unthinkable and unbearable losses and can be accompanied by feelings of guilt and depression. I was fortunate enough to experience neither of these heart-wrenching outcomes, but for the women who have, there is a level of grief that never leaves their heart or mind for the rest of their lives. A life was growing in their womb and suddenly taken away without any warning and without their consent. How do you cope with such a loss? How do you learn to trust your body again? How do you let go of the blame you put on yourself? How do you believe there is a God?

While we often only relate loss to the former, loss can also look like: having an unsuccessful treatment, embryos that didn't survive, or a failed IVF transfer. Infertility can create the loss of friendships, relationships, and in some cases, a marriage. The feeling of loss is such a profound, deep pain. It can be entirely overwhelming. When most people experience loss: of a partner, a pet, a job, a house, they're usually losing "something." During the infertility journey, the loss you feel can be confusing as you may not have physically lost anything. You may simply feel you have lost or may lose the opportunity to become a mother.

There is great loss in infertility, but there is also great love. There was love as your baby was growing and that love remains even after the loss. The love for your husband and the love for the unborn child you pray for holds immense power to overcome the loss.

Despite all the range of emotions felt in my infertility journey, my actions were driven by love and propelled me forward. With love comes forgiveness. The losses we experience in each of our infertility struggles require us to forgive ourselves and, in turn, pour more love into our journey.

Hope in Loss

FEELINGS OF LOSS come after a miscarriage or even a negative pregnancy test, when it's month after month. This battle with infertility may lead to discouragement and depression. But if you allow God, he will comfort you with his presence and assure you that you'll never be without help and empowerment (Isaiah 41:10). God cares for the broken-hearted and those in pain (Psalm 34:18). He will bring healing and strength (Psalm 73:26). Know that his love for you is unreserved and unconditional and there's absolutely nothing that can separate you from his care and affection.

Loss is a part of grieving. Don't ignore the pain you feel. Let it run through your blood, let the tears fall, let the deep emptiness sit in your heart. Patience is a virtue and is something you need to allow yourself plenty of. Part of dealing with loss is accepting what you cannot change. One day, you'll wake up and celebrate life again. You will. Look on the bright side of things and try to do something meaningful, even if it's for just five minutes. Express your daily gratitude for the blessings present in your life.

However you experience and view loss during infertility, hope in the assurance that our Creator and Lifegiver, who holds all things together, will work everything out for your good.

NOTES

NUMB: GOING THROUGH THE
MOTIONS

For if our heart condemns us, God is greater than
our heart, and knoweth all things.

— 1 JOHN 3:20 (KJV)

"You ou have to accept the fact that you may
never get pregnant with your uterus." I
will never forget these words spoken by
my first fertility doctor after I expressed my anguish
over our failed IUIs. He let out a laugh when I started
crying and said I shouldn't cry because only 8 percent
of couples achieve success through IUI. I had been
diagnosed with having a T-shaped uterus which
makes it extremely difficult to conceive and a height-
ened risk of not being able to carry full term. I had

just gone through several unsuccessful IUIs, and now I felt like it had all been a big joke . . . at my expense.

I left that appointment feeling emotionally numb. I wasn't sad or angry. I felt absolutely nothing. When I returned home, I laid in bed and I could feel that this was not the answer. This was not my fate. This was not the end. I decided I didn't have to take this doctor's word for it. I didn't have to go along with his plan or prognosis. I was under God's plan.

Fast forward to several months later and my new fertility doctor determined that I did not have a T-shaped uterus after all! While I did have other underlying issues, this discovery was a huge relief. This situation served as a reminder to me that man does not have the final say over our health, our fertility, or our future—only God does, and submitting our ways unto him will lead us to the right path.

When was the last time you felt something? A common emotion associated with the infertility journey, whether at the beginning or in the middle. You don't feel anything. You're there, but you are not present. You're going through the motions but not enjoying the brilliant fall morning or embracing the sensation of soft grass under your feet or feeling the sun against your back as you sip your coffee. Your body goes into a state of numbness to protect itself from the deep pain you're feeling underneath it all.

The inability to conceive can make you go numb and numbness often goes hand in hand with depression. It can suck the life or feeling out of you where you seem to just withdraw from life and emotion. You become reclusive and won't participate. You can't find a reason to celebrate. Nothing sparks joy. You engage in no activities, you have no reactions, not even a smile. You just feel deadness. While this is a normal emotion to feel during this journey (at any point), it's important to talk to a counselor if these feelings don't lift at all. Many fantastic counselors specialize in women's trauma and grief. You don't need to go through this alone or feel the way that you do long-term.

Hope in Numbness

THERE'S HOPE IN NUMBNESS. In the dead of night, light and life can come. Hope can help you achieve miraculous things. A burning hope and trust can lighten your mind and body. It can bring you to health and nourishment and raise a womb that can carry the child you so long for. In the Bible, Sarah was way past the child-bearing age but she kept in mind that God is faithful and that he can do great and miraculous things. In hope, she carried on and God gave her Isaac. So, remember, "It is the Lord who goes before you; He will be with you. He will not fail you or abandon you. Do not fear or be dismayed." (Deuteronomy. 31:8 AMP)

NOTES

SHAME: HOW WILL OTHERS SEE ME?

For the Lord God will help me; therefore shall I not be confounded: therefore have I set my face like a flint, and I know that I shall not be ashamed.

— ISAIAH 50:7 (KJV)

I saw it over and over in my head and sometimes in my dreams . . . the woman people would whisper about that could never have children. The woman they pitied. The woman they didn't invite to parties where kids would be present. That woman was me. I became flooded with shame. With that shame came feelings of failure and embarrassment. Was I a disgrace? I didn't want to feel less than the average woman who was able to procreate. I didn't want to be that woman.

Infertility can be a shameful thing when we focus on what others are thinking of us or how they view our infertile status. Over time, I affirmed that how others saw me didn't matter. I have a God who sees me as beautiful, strong, and blossoming, and there is no room for shame in his eyes. This acceptance and love removed the shame I felt and allowed me to share my journey and embrace the human parts of me.

You are not a failure, even though you may tell yourself you are. "I have failed at the one basic thing I was put on earth to do as a woman." "I am worried that this reflects on my relationship." "Does this reflect on my sex life?" These are common thoughts and questions that play in the mind of a woman on the infertility journey. We often feel like we are our feelings, and if these feelings aren't "right," we fear we become them.

Look at yourself in the mirror. What do you see? Do you see a strong woman whose body has been through a lot, yet is still here, standing in all of her glory? Do you see a woman whose determination to succeed and ability to never give up is grounded in her? Do you see a woman who, one day, whichever way this may be, will make a fantastic mother? Do you?

Hope in Shame

CHILDLESSNESS CAN BRING SHAME, especially when all your family and friends have biological kids. You start to feel inadequate, even inferior to these parents around you. You become shameful. You consider yourself a failure because you've failed to live up to expectations. But there's hope in shame. You need not hide your face. Don't belittle yourself, because you're greatly loved by our heavenly Father. And to him, you're perfect as you are right now. He looks at you with assuring eyes that say you are "fearfully and wonderfully made." (Psalm 139:14)

Stay hopeful. Take heart. Trust that God will grant your request in his time. Keep hoping and never dwindle. Keep asking. Keep seeking. Knock until the door opens. And while you wait for your little one, say no to shame. Find security in divine love. Remember that God's unfailing love will always be with you and for you. It's as strong now as it ever will be (Jeremiah 31:3).

NOTES

SHOCKED: AN UNWELCOME SURPRISE

Let not your heart be troubled: ye believe in God, believe also in me.

— JOHN 14:1 (KJV)

There are many things that may come as a shock on your infertility journey. Can I tell you what shocked me the most (besides realizing I couldn't get pregnant)? The rollercoaster of emotions. Why didn't anyone warn me?

The person I was prior to experiencing infertility was strong, confident, stable, motivated, resilient, level-headed, determined, and unemotional. I could not believe the first time I broke down and cried over my inability to conceive. The woman who didn't even cry during sad movies sat sobbing loudly with tears streaming down her face. Who was this person? I didn't know it then, but this was the start of a rebirth for me. You see, sometimes God has to shed layers off of us and peel back corners to reveal who we really are and his purpose for us. Experiencing the wide range of emotions described in this book has made me feel more human. Sometimes, to be truly authentic requires a bearing of our soul in a shocking and uncomfortable way.

Many women are not aware that they're infertile or will find it challenging to conceive. You want to have a baby, start a family. You're ready, your partner is too, and all that's left to do is . . . get pregnant. But why aren't your test results coming up as positive? This isn't how it was supposed to be. You have your life planned, and a child is a crucial part of that life.

Repeated failings can suspend you in a state and cycle of shock. You feel sick even when you're healthy. You can't think straight; no one and nothing makes sense. No pep talk can make you feel better. You lose control and awareness of your body. It's like you're disconnected from everyone and everything. You feel a surge of emotions. You want to scream; and maybe, you do. But you just can't snap out of it.

You don't know how and where to run. Or worse, you feel lost and can't find your way back.

Feeling shocked is normal. It's an emotional state your body goes into when it has either witnessed something horrific or heard some terrible news. Remember, shock is a temporary feeling. It's something that appears initially but usually fades away over time. Shock can send you into a dark place. But you know what the beautiful part of finding yourself in that dark place is? You can finally see the stars. Focus on the benefits, not just the difficulties, and learn from the experience.

Hope in Shock

UNDERSTAND that there's no expectation for you to act normally after a failed pregnancy. And it may take a lot of time to bounce back from disappointment. But know that there is hope in shock. And with hope, there is no trauma you cannot recover from. "The God of all grace . . . after you have suffered a little while, will himself restore you and make you strong, firm, and steadfast." (1 Peter 5:10 NIV) There's no escaping; you will endure a period of suffering. But

God promises that his grace will prove sufficient for your situation (2 Corinthians 12:9). Don't deny yourself the sadness. Feel it, accept it. Then release it and nurture yourself back to joy and hope; for God is able to make you strong (Romans 12:15). And he will.

NOTES

SAD: DEEPLY, TRULY

For his anger endureth but a moment; in his favour is life: weeping may endure for a night but joy cometh in the morning.

— PSALM 30:5 (KJV)

Sadness was the strongest emotion I felt during infertility. To describe it would be to describe grief. I can recount all the things that made me feel sad on the surface. Shopping for baby items for others, seeing a pregnant woman, watching diaper commercials, seeing a mother with her children, seeing a baby, pregnancy announcements, gender reveals, unrelenting social media bump posts, seeing the look in my husband's eyes as he tried to convince me that everything would be fine. But the sadness is much deeper than that. It's not just in your heart or pit of your stomach. It feels like it is in every organ, running through your veins. It's a constant sadness, even when a smile is on your face. It's attached to everything you see, do, or hear and a part of every day. It's even present when you are intimate with your spouse.

This sadness truly caught me off guard and left me feeling broken and lost in darkness. Studies have shown that infertile women experience the same level of anxiety and depression as those suffering from a chronic illness. While this knowledge validated my feelings, it didn't alleviate them. I needed something that was life-giving. This is when my love for daily devotionals developed. I found ones specific to infertility and reading the words of comfort felt like receiving a big hug each morning. I started looking forward to each day's message and watched as peace and hope began to rebuild my fragile spirit. Evening walks, a greater appreciation for nature, practicing mindfulness and gratitude also became routine for me.

The sadness may remain for many years but the weight of it can be lifted by doing things that speak to our soul.

This feeling of sadness can come upon you when trying to conceive just doesn't happen. And when infertility persists, sadness may grow piercing claws, clinging to you, restricting you, even isolating you. Quite soon, sadness may bring with it the pangs of loneliness. Yes, you are with people who love and support you. Your spouse is there, but even around them, you may be unable to shake the deep and aching sadness that looms over your heart.

What must you do to free yourself from this? If conceiving is the solution and it hasn't come for so long, does that mean you're doomed to months and years of sadness? Does that mean you need to put on a brave face in public for a long time? Does that mean you have to dismiss it or deny it exists? No. Going down that road may not be the best recourse.

You know you don't have to pretend it isn't there. You don't need to hide behind a fake smile. Don't hide what you feel and don't be ashamed of it. More importantly, don't give in and don't face it alone. Share them with those closest to you, especially your spouse or partner in life. Those who've been with you through thick and thin, open yourself to them and allow them to live this trying time with you. And when you're alone, know that there is someone who wants to comfort you in your time of sadness and inability to conceive.

Hope in Sadness

THERE ARE things that may be too hard to understand, things like not being given a baby when you so want it above all things. But remember, you don't need to rack your brain right now and try to understand the reason nor the purpose for this hardship. But to work your way through the sadness and loneliness, you do need to understand that God's love is for you and he is there. He knows what you're going through. Sadness reminds us we'll see better days ahead.

In Psalm 25, David, the King, a man devoted to God, was going through some tough times. In this song, we can see him struggling with sadness, fear, doubt, and more. In this song, we also see that choosing to trust God kept him going. David sings, "In You, I put my trust."

Like David, you can choose to trust God to see you through this. Trust that he is good and that he loves you, that even without a baby right now, you are, more than ever, precious in his sight, so valued by him. Stay your mind upon him and let him bring rest and release, even in your saddest and most difficult moments. And, like David, you can be bare and open before God. Like David, you can ask your heavenly Father to, "Turn to me and be gracious to me, for I am lonely and afflicted. Relieve the troubles of my heart and free me from my anguish."

NOTES

SURRENDER: QUE SERA SERA

And he said, My presence shall go with thee, and I will give thee rest.

— EXODUS 33:14 (KJV)

I remember the day clearly. The day I surrendered to the process, to a plan other than mine. I had been driving myself crazy with worry for years and decided enough was enough. I needed to get away from my thoughts and from the weight of pain. I took the three-hour drive to Salvation Mountain. The air was still as it neared sunset. The atmosphere was calm and peaceful. I chose a bench behind an old truck and I sat alone and prayed.

This time, I didn't pray for a baby. I prayed for

God's will to be done over my life; for him to use me in this trial. An undeniable peace washed over me in that moment. I didn't know if I'd ever be a mother, but I was certain that God had something amazing in store for me. It was the first time in nearly three years that I exhaled. Could it be possible that I could actually develop, grow, mature, progress, evolve, flourish, thrive, prosper, and bloom during this season of waiting in hope? Yes.

No man or woman can fully grasp the pain of a miscarriage or of enduring months and years of waiting to conceive. Pain is unique to all. Each seeming defeat can cause the soul to sink further into the depths of despair and bitter surrender. Ah, surrender! Acceptance! These can be flowery words—seemingly beautiful—yet, they're more likely detestable to those who are coping with infertility or loss. Why? Because they don't get to choose. The husband and wife are forced to battle a burning pain that continues long after they've surrendered.

The inability to conceive will bring the strongest of women to her knees. And sometimes, that is where you need to end up in order to relinquish control of the situation. Once you surrender, you will see that you are exactly where you need to be and there is a story that has been written uniquely for you.

Hope in Surrender

THERE IS HOPE IN SURRENDER, for where man fails to fully empathize, God comes to your aid. He fully knows, and he fully feels for you. And if you must surrender, then surrender not in weakness but in full trust, "And we know that all things work together for good to those who love God." (Romans 8:28 NKJV) Trust in him to direct your steps and know that his plans for you will never fail you. So, come to him in all your weakness and leave his presence in all strength. Believe, as Paul did and experienced in 1 Corinthians 10:12, that when you come to God in your weakness, you will overcome, and you will be made strong.

NOTES

EPILOGUE

We welcomed our son, Kai Dennis Oberon, on July 16, 2018, after our second round of *in vitro* fertilization. After nearly four years, this was our last attempt to conceive before considering fostering or adoption. We still have six frozen embryos but are undecided as to whether we will go through IVF again, following complications in pregnancy and postpartum. Our initial plan was to attempt to conceive naturally following the birth of Kai, but we all know what God thinks about our plans! We continue to build our faith in whether it is God's will to grow our family, but are presently at peace knowing we wanted a single chance to be parents, and Kai chose us for that very purpose.

We had this thing called hope, and it carried us through. Grateful does not even begin to describe how we feel every single day as parents, and we continue to pray for other couples to find renewed strength and hope in their own unique journeys.

ACKNOWLEDGMENTS

To the many women on their journey to motherhood who have inspired me to write this book, and to my husband who has been my source of strength and inspiration during our own infertility journey. Thank you all for igniting a passion in me to instill hope during a hopeless time.

ABOUT THE AUTHOR

Christina Oberon was born and raised in Oahu, Hawaii before moving to Los Angeles. She and her husband married in 2014 and went through four years of infertility and multiple rounds of fertility treatments before conceiving their son, Kai, via in vitro fertiliza-

tion. During the Oberons' infertility journey, Christina became passionate about encouraging and supporting other women on their journey to motherhood and continues to be active in the infertility community hoping to empower, uplift, and instill hope in those suffering from the heartache that infertility brings.

65116006R00086

Made in the USA
Middletown, DE
02 September 2019